Bond

No.1 for exam success

English and **Verbal Reasoning**

Assessment Papers

CEM
(Durham University)

8–9 years

OXFORD

UNIVERSITY PRESS

OXFORD
UNIVERSITY PRESS

Great Clarendon Street, Oxford, OX2 6DP, United Kingdom

Oxford University Press is a department of the University of Oxford. It furthers the University's objective of excellence in research, scholarship, and education by publishing worldwide. Oxford is a registered trade mark of Oxford University Press in the UK and in certain other countries

British Library Cataloguing in Publication Data
Data available

978-0-1927-4282-7
10 9 8 7 6 5 4 3 2

Paper used in the production of this book is a natural, recyclable product made from wood grown in sustainable forests. The manufacturing process conforms to the environmental regulations of the country of origin.

Printed in China

Acknowledgements

Page make-up: Tech-Set Ltd, Gateshead
Illustrations: Beehive Illustration
Cover illustrations: Lo Cole

Although we have made every effort to trace and contact all copyright holders before publication this has not been possible in all cases.
If notified, the publisher will rectify any errors or omissions at the earliest opportunity.

Links to third party websites are provided by Oxford in good faith and for information only. Oxford disclaims any responsibility for the materials contained in any third party website referenced in this work.

Before you get started

What is Bond?

This book is part of the Bond CEM Assessment Papers series for English and Verbal Reasoning, which provides **thorough and continuous practice of key English and Verbal Reasoning skills** from ages eight to eleven. Bond's resources are ideal preparation for Key Stage 1 and Key Stage 2 SATs, the 11+, the CEE and other selective school entrance exams.

How does the scope of this book match real exam content?

Each paper is carefully pitched to ensure a smooth progression towards the next level. Unlike other 11+ papers, the CEM exam is a combination of literacy **and** verbal reasoning questions. They cover comprehension, vocabulary, spellings, grammar and logical reasoning, with a higher emphasis on word knowledge. The question format is much more varied and this holistic approach to learning key skills, rather than learning question styles, will also provide a rigorous foundation for other exams.

The coverage of grammar, vocabulary, comprehension and spellings is matched to the National Curriculum and the National Literacy Strategy and will also **provide invaluable preparation for Key Stage 2 SATs**. The aim of the CEM exam is to constantly change the style and format of questions. This makes it outside of the scope of any book to provide a prescriptive series of papers, but the Bond CEM Assessment Papers are based on the range and styles of questions asked in previous exams alongside a solid foundation of the **key skills that will underpin the CEM exams**.

Some schools may also include a written composition as part of the 11+ exam. Although it is outside the scope of this book to practise extended and creative writing skills, *Bond Focus on Writing* provides full coverage of writing skills.

What does the book contain?

- **6 papers** – each one contains 75 questions.
- **Tutorial links throughout** – 📖 – this icon appears in the margin next to the questions. It indicates links to the relevant section in *How To Do CEM English and Verbal Reasoning*, our invaluable subject guide that offers explanations and practice for all core question types.

- **Scoring devices** – there are score boxes in the margins and a Progress Chart on page 60. The chart is a visual and motivating way for children to see how they are doing. It also turns the score into a percentage that can help inform what to do next.
- **Answers** – located in an easily-removed central pull-out section.

How can you use this book?

One of the great strengths of Bond Assessment Papers is their flexibility. They can be used at home, in school and by tutors to:

- set **timed formal practice** tests – allow about 45 minutes per paper in line with standard 11+ demands. Gradually reduce the suggested time limit by ten minutes to practise working at speed
- provide **bite-sized chunks** for regular practice
- **highlight strengths and weaknesses** in the core skills
- identify **individual needs**
- set **homework**
- follow **a complete 11+ preparation strategy** alongside *The Parents' Guide to the 11+* (see below).

It is best to start at the beginning and work through the papers in order to make the best use of the Progress Chart. If you are using the book as part of a careful run-in to the 11+, we suggest that you also have three or four other essential Bond resources close at hand:

- *How To Do CEM English and Verbal Reasoning*: the subject guide that explains all the question types practised in this book. Use the cross-reference icons to find the relevant sections.

- *The Parents' Guide to the 11+*: the step-by-step guide to the whole 11+ experience. It clearly explains the 11+ process, provides guidance on how to assess children, helps you to set complete action plans for practice and explains how you can use *CEM English and Verbal Reasoning 8–9* as part of a strategic run-in to the exam.

- *Focus on Comprehension*: the practical handbook that clearly shows children how to read and understand the text, understand the questions and assess their own answers.

- *Focus on Writing*: the essential resource that explains the key components of successful writing.

What does a score mean and how can it be improved?

It is unfortunately impossible to guarantee that a child will pass the 11+ exam if they achieve a certain score on any practice book or paper. Success on the day depends on a host of factors, including the scores of the other children sitting the test. However, we can provide invaluable guidance on what a score indicates and how to improve it.

If children colour in the Progress Chart on page 60, this will give an idea of present performance in percentage terms. The Next Steps Planner inside the back cover will help you to decide what to do next to help a child progress. It is always valuable to go over wrong answers with children. If they are having trouble with any particular question type, follow the tutorial links to *How To Do CEM English and Verbal Reasoning* for step-by-step explanations and further practice. Bond offers the complete range of resources for you and your child, to give you the maximum support that you need.

Don't forget the website …!

Visit www.bond11plus.co.uk for lots of advice, information and suggestions on everything to do with Bond, the 11+ and helping children to achieve their best.

Key words

Some special words are used in this book. You will find them in **bold** each time they appear in the Papers. These words are explained here.

adjective	a word that describes someone or something
adverb	a word that describes an action
antonym	a word with a meaning opposite to another word, for example *wet* and *dry*
conjunction	a word that links sentences phrases or words, for example *and, because*
contraction	two words shortened into one with the use of an apostrophe, *it is = it's*
definition	the meaning of a word
homophone	a word that has the same sound as another but with a different meaning or spelling, for example *pain, pane*
noun	a word for someone or something
past tense	the form of a verb showing something that has already happened
present tense	the form of a verb showing something that is happening now
pronoun	a word that replaces a noun, for example *him, her, it, they*
root word	a word that can have a prefix or suffix added to it, for example un<u>friend</u>ly
sentence	a group of words that makes sense standing alone
simile	an expression that describes something as being like something else, for example *the sun was as round as a golden coin*
singular	one of something, for example *man*
stanza	poems can be divided into blocks of poetry called stanzas
synonym	a word with a meaning similar to another word, for example *smile, grin*
verb	an action or doing word

Paper 1

Read the following comprehension text and answer the questions that follow it.

Charlie and Me

Charlie is my favourite friend,
We go everywhere together.
He makes me laugh, he makes me smile,
We'll be friends forever.

5   I have fair hair, he has brown.
He always smiles, I often frown.
He is always trying to cheer me up,
When I am feeling down.

Last year we both went camping,
10   A site beside the sea,
We watched the stars, we heard the waves,
As happy as could be.

We visited a castle, the beach
And a hilltop zoo,
15   We laughed so much together
As we usually do.

To find a friend like Charlie,
I know is really rare.
Charlie is my favourite friend,
20   He's my oldest teddy bear.

1 What type of creature is Charlie?

_____

2 Find three examples that show us this is a poem.

_____

_____

_____

3 Which four places does Charlie visit?

_____

_____

_____

4 The word 'site' (line 10) is a **homophone** with the word 'sight' because they sound the same but have different spellings and a different meaning. Can you find another word in the same **stanza** that is also a **homophone**?

_____

5 Which one phrase is repeated?

_____

_____

6 Find three ways in which Charlie is such a good friend.

_____

_____

_____

7 The words 'we will' are joined with an apostrophe to make 'we'll' in the first stanza. This is called a **contraction**. Which two words are joined together in the same way in the last stanza?

_____

Look at the following words and then use them to answer the questions that follow.

team	mass	needle	real	proud
crowd	straw	prince	coast	reward
polite	growl	remain	depart	narrow
praise	leave	thin	wonder	stay
slender	pack	gradual	front	beach

8 Find two words that are **synonyms** for the word 'shore'.

_____

9 Find three words that are **antonyms** for the word 'wide'.

_____

_____

10 Find four words that are **synonyms** for the word 'group'.

_____

_____

_____

11 Find two words that are **antonyms** for the word 'arrive'.

_____

12 Find two words that are **antonyms** for the word 'punish'.

_____

Underline the two odd words out in the following groups of words

Example   purple   lilac   <u>olive</u   <u>sage</u   violet

13 huge   big   tiny   little   small

14 magazine   book   newspaper   television   radio

15 freezing   icy   boiling   hot   cold

16 heart   hand   liver   elbow   kidney

17 car   coach   bus   driver   passenger

18 milk   yoghurt   cheese   bread   cake

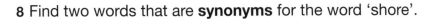

13

6

9

Write the **singular** version of these words in these **sentences**.

Example   Where is the ___cat___ ? (cats)

19 Lil lives in a _____ (houses) with a blue door.

20 There is a _____ (churches) at the end of our street.

21 Only one _____ (children) scored top marks.

22 Trevor has a new _____ (scarves) to wear in the cold weather.

23 We've had our dog since he was a _____ (puppies).

24 There is a _____ (flies) in my drink.

25 Brooke has her _____ (lunches) at school.

Find the three letters that complete these words. The three letters do not have to make a word.

Example   fr<u>es</u>h spl<u>as</u>h

26 addr_____ es   _____ ncess

27 pun_____ ed   donk_____

28 _____ derful   brin_____ g

29 tea_____ rs   stoc_____ gs

30 p_____ aps   po_____ ar

Find the three-letter word that can be added to the letters in capitals to make a new word. The new word will complete the **sentence** sensibly.

Example   We HED the keys to the estate agent.   <u>AND</u>

31 The twins needed to behave TSELVES. _____

32 I have a new pen for WRIG with. _____

33 The wind was BING strongly. _____

34 The sun was behind me casting long SOWS. _____

35 Grandma makes lovely sticky toffee PUDG. _____

36 That star is the BHTEST in the sky. _____

6

9 mins

2 D

Underline the one word on the right that has the most opposite meaning to the word on the left.

Example	**rose**	thorn	flower	<u>fell</u>	down	up
37 accidental	clumsy	deliberate	dangerous	mistaken	occasion
38 certain	unsure	sure	insure	reassure	assure
39 increase	include	creased	shrink	grow	large
40 minute	second	hour	tiny	huge	medium
41 ordinary	plain	expected	reduced	normal	unusual
42 smooth	silky	sleek	average	rough	dirty

6

Complete each **sentence** by selecting the best word from the options **a, b, c, d** or **e**.

3 E

Example   People travelling to certain countries need ___d – vaccination___ .

a	**b**	**c**	**d**	**e**
immunity	certainty	vacation	vaccination	respiration

43 There was so much work to do I was kept _____

a	**b**	**c**	**d**	**e**
quick	slow	busy	noisy	quite

44 Our teacher is _____ but she is fair and we do work hard.

a	**b**	**c**	**d**	**e**
strict	mean	teaching	nice	unfair

45 There are one hundred years in a _____

a	**b**	**c**	**d**	**e**
decade	century	kilometre	millennium	dozen

46 I took the _____ that the doctor had prescribed.

a	**b**	**c**	**d**	**e**
medicine	drink	food	question	nurse

4

Read the following **sentences** and answer the questions. Underline the correct answer.

3 G

Example 'The plane's departure time was 13:45.'
What does the word 'departure' mean? Answer: **b**

a	**b**	**c**	**d**
arriving	<u>leaving</u>	resting	mending

47 'We meet every Wednesday and occasionally on a Friday night.'
What does 'occasionally' mean?

a	**b**	**c**	**d**
party	never	always	sometimes

48 'We have a dog to guard our house.'
What does 'guard' mean?

a	**b**	**c**	**d**
protect	find	betray	entertain

49 'What is that peculiar smell?'
What does 'peculiar' mean?

a	**b**	**c**	**d**
beautiful	horrible	strange	sweet

50 'Perhaps we will go to the library later.'
What does 'perhaps' mean?

a	**b**	**c**	**d**
promise	maybe	definitely	doubtful

4

Rearrange these words to make the longest **sentence** you can. Underline the one word that is not needed.

3 H

Example So cream <u>eat</u> the were cakes delicious.
The cream cakes were so delicious.

51 In a cinema are there circus artists trapeze.

_____

52 The leg wagged his little dog tail.

_____

53 The bakery had no Vikings about the books library.

_____

54 Handbag queen gold wore crown her the.

_____

55 Five divide three add two makes.

_____

56 Our teachers has six classroom tables in it.

_____

6

Add the missing letters to the word on the right to make a word with the most similar meaning to the word on the left.

2C 3C

Example   vision   s <u>i</u> <u>g</u> <u>h</u>t

57 wash   c __ __ an

58 ill   __ o __ r __ y

59 heat   wa __ __ __ h

60 big   __ __ __ ge

61 tall   h__ __ h

62 style   f __ s __ i __ n

63 cut   sn__ __

7

Take a different **conjunction** from the box and place it in a space so that each **sentence** makes sense.

| because | but | or | so | yet |

64 Kayleigh was reading a book _____ she should have been putting her toys away.

65 Jodie was tired _____ she went to bed late last night.

66 Would you like an orange _____ would you prefer an apple?

67 He is ten now _____ he is old enough to know better.

68 That film is my favourite _____ I've never seen the sequel.

The underlined words in this paragraph have not been spelled correctly. Write out the misspelled words in the right-hand box, so that the spellings are correct and the paragraph makes sense. The first word has been done for you.

The <u>vickson</u> slunk <u>behynd</u> the tree trunk and into her den. The dying sun shone <u>throow</u> her red hair, making it glow like burnished copper. She was <u>tiered</u> and very fat. As the sun rose the next <u>mornin</u>, the vixen <u>yawnd</u> and <u>streched</u> out. Three newborn cubs were <u>hungery</u>. They blinked in the sunlight, ready to start their first day.	e.g. vixen
	69
	70
	71
	72
	73
	74
	75

Now go to the Progress Chart to record your score!   Total   90

Paper 2

Look at the following words and then use them to answer the questions that follow.

sow	claw	borrow	howl	burst
yell	nail	scream	shape	clean
deal	field	rather	trade	young
safe	cooler	cheer	grief	spotless
sparkling	plant	decoration	harmless	pattern

1 Find three words that are **synonyms** for the word 'design'.

_____

_____

2 Find two words that are **antonyms** for the word 'dangerous'.

_____

3 Find three words that are **synonyms** for the word 'shout'.

_____

_____

4 Find three words that are **antonyms** for the word 'dirty'.

_____

_____

5 Find two words that are **synonyms** for the word 'talon'.

_____

2 A

2 B

2 A

2 B

2 A

13

Rearrange these words to make the longest **sentence** you can. Underline the one word that is not needed.

3 H

Example   So cream <u>eat</u> the were cakes delicious.
              The cream cakes were so delicious.

6 Wash your feet before need to sandwiches making you hands.

_____

15

7 The garden shed we planted a rose in bush.

_____

8 Denim are often wood made jeans from.

_____

9 The space was running bus to late town.

_____

10 The boats returned with full coaches fishermen.

_____

5

Add the missing letters to the word on the right to make a word with the most similar meaning to the word on the left.

2C 3C

Example   vision   s _i_ _g_ _h_ t

11 pants   t __ o __ s __ r __

12 cold   ch __ __ __y

13 entire   w __ o __e

14 share   __ i __ i __e

15 sound   n __ __se

16 brush   sw __ __ __

6

Find the three-letter word that can be added to the letters in capitals to make a new word. The new word will complete the **sentence** sensibly.

3 A

Example   We HED the keys to the estate agent. <u>AND</u>

17 With a new moon, the night is DER than usual. _____

18 Today in school we LNT about the Tudors. _____

19 Have you BORED my red crayon? _____

20 Would you RAR have grapes or an apple with your cheese?

_____

21 Root vegetables include carrots, swedes and TIPS. _____

22 People that we do not know are called STGERS. _____

23 My friends enjoy roller SKAG but I keep falling over! _____ ⬤ 7

2 F

Underline the two odd words out in the following groups of words.

Example   purple   lilac   <u>olive</u>   <u>sage</u>   violet

24 kitten   puppy   giraffe   elephant   hippopotamus

25 nose   mouth   eyes   fingers   toes

26 rice   plate   pasta   bowl   dish

27 hear   walk   ears   legs   talk

28 earring   bracelet   necklace   gold   silver   ⬤ 5

Write the **singular** version of the words in these **sentences**.

4 A

Example   Where is the ____cat____ ? (cats)

29 There is a _____ (foxes) hunting for food.

30 There is a new _____ (shops) in our village.

31 Michael wears a school _____ (ties) to look smart.

32 What is in that big _____ (boxes)?

33 Lucy has a white pet _____ (mice) called Jerry.   ⬤ 5

Underline the one word on the right that has the most opposite meaning to the word on the left.

15 mins
2 D

Example   rose   thorn   flower   <u>fell</u>   down   up

34 important   vital   main   irrelevant   key   strict

35 whole   complete   part   central   finished   ended

36 often   rarely   frequent   many   few   always

17

37 **answer**	reply	regret	exclaim	question	write
38 **catch**	drop	crawl	fall	net	problem
39 **stop**	end	cease	crease	go	arrive
40 **enough**	lots	scarce	increased	decreased	ought

7

Complete each **sentence** by selecting the best word from the options **a**, **b**, **c**, **d** or **e**.

3 E

Example   People travelling to certain countries need ___ **d – vaccination** ___ .

a	b	c	d	e
immunity	certainty	vacation	vaccination	respiration

41 There was a large _____ of girls at the park.

a	b	c	d	e
group	litter	pack	herd	flock

42 The _____ dog dragged the clean clothes from the washing line.

a	b	c	d	e
sleeping	friendly	sensible	brave	naughty

43 We were asked to _____ what our perfect holiday would be like.

a	b	c	d	e
talk	imagine	remember	prefer	visit

44 Michael likes a _____ of fruit such as pears, berries and bananas.

a	b	c	d	e
library	bowl	variety	few	select

45 To bake this cake we need to _____ the egg white from the yolk.

a	b	c	d	e
desperate	exaggerate	separate	multiply	add

46 In Brownies we made our _____ to serve our community.

a	b	c	d	e
promise	threat	shout	cry	question

○ 6

A **homophone** is a word that sounds like another but has a different spelling. Underline the one **homophone** in each line.

📖 1 E

Example   wish   <u>war</u>   when   wicket   welcome   (war and wore)

47 red   yellow   green   orange   black

48 cod   haddock   plaice   salmon   halibut

49 novel   new   fresh   ripe   young

50 cover   clothe   conceal   wear   blanket

51 three   five   seven   two   nine

52 drank   ate   swallowed   chewed   devoured

○ 6

The underlined words in this paragraph have not been spelled correctly. Write out the misspelled words in the right-hand box, so that the spellings are correct and the paragraph makes sense. The first word has been done for you.

📖 1 E

To make a Sorrento <u>Smoothey</u> you need the <u>folowing</u> ingredients: ten <u>strawberys</u>, two <u>appels</u>, one <u>bannaanna</u>, two peaches (take the stones out), two <u>scoowps</u> of <u>vannilar</u> ice cream and one litre of milk. Blend the <u>frute</u> and milk together in a liquidiser to make the smoothie base. Pour half of it into a tall glass, add the ice cream and top up with the rest of the smoothie base.	e.g. smoothie 53 54 55 56 57 58 59

 ○ 7

Read the following comprehension text and then answer the questions that follow it.

Pals of the Parrotfish

The huge parrotfish is over a metre long and can change its colour from the brightest blues and greens to pinks, oranges and yellows. They have
5   lots of teeth that are tightly packed together, making their jawbones look like a parrot's beak. These teeth allow them to munch away at coral and rock, as well as the occasional little fish.
10 Parrotfish can form a protective layer when they go to sleep at night, but as this mucus layer is brightly coloured, it looks as though the parrotfish is wearing pyjamas! Although parrotfish
15 look pretty and amusing to us, they must look very scary to other fish and that is where their little mates come in.

The goby fish is smaller than 10 centimetres long, although some species are less than 10 millimetres long, making them some of the
20 smallest fish in the world. These peaceful little fish are sometimes called the 'cleaner' or 'doctor' fish for one clever reason. When the big parrotfish has eaten well, its teeth get full of food that begins to rot. How would your teeth feel if you never brushed them? Well, this is how the parrotfish feels, but it doesn't have a toothbrush or toothpaste.
25 What the parrotfish does have is the tiny goby.

The parrotfish swims up to the little goby and shows its buddy that there is no danger of being eaten. The little fish swims up to the giant parrotfish's mouth and swims in and out, nibbling at the rotten flesh of the parrotfish to keep it healthy and gobbling up the food that is stuck
30 to the parrotfish's teeth until they are as clean as a new pin.

The parrotfish leaves with nice clean teeth and no rotting flesh. The goby is very happy to have a tummy full of food without having to go and hunt for it. The parrotfish and the goby both need each other and this makes them surprising, but firm friends.

60 What are the three words used in the extract that mean the same as 'friend'?

6 mins

1 C

3

61 How do you think the parrotfish gets its name?

_____

_____

62 Why does the mucus layer look like the parrotfish is wearing pyjamas?

_____

63 When and why does the parrotfish form a mucus layer?

_____

_____

64 Why do you think the goby fish is called the 'cleaner' or 'doctor' fish?

_____

_____

65 Can you find a **simile** in the third paragraph?

_____

66 What do these words mean as used in the text? Provide a **definition**.

   a munch (line 8) _____

   b tummy (line 32) _____

   c firm (line 34) _____

67 Give two reasons why the parrotfish and goby are friends.

_____

_____

_____

Read the following **sentences** and answer the questions. Underline the correct answer.

Example   'The plane's departure time was 13:45.'
           What does the word 'departure' mean? Answer: **b**

a	**b**	**c**	**d**
arriving	<u>leaving</u>	resting	mending

21

68 'I feel sick, therefore I won't go to the park.'
   What does 'therefore' mean?

a	**b**	**c**	**d**
so	and	but	because

69 'Adam is working hard for his exams so he is feeling pressure.'
   What does 'pressure' mean?

a	**b**	**c**	**d**
happy	sad	stress	tired

70 'The receptionist is at the heart of this school.'
   What does 'heart' mean?

a	**b**	**c**	**d**
skin	peel	core	seed

71 'The old bathroom was really grimy.'
   What does 'grimy' mean?

a	**b**	**c**	**d**
ancient	dirty	cool	unfashionable

4

Find the three letters that complete these words. The three letters do not have to make a word.

3 B

Example   fr<u>esh</u> spl<u>as</u>h

72 r_____bow   c_____ken

73 _____erstood   borr_____d

74 som_____mes   pud_____g

75 darl_____   fi_____ork

4

Now go to the Progress Chart to record your score!   Total   90

Paper 3

Read the following comprehension text and answer the questions that follow it.

The Long Night

Ernie was extremely annoyed. Father Christmas had asked everyone to work overtime to make sure everything was ready for the Long Night. Ernie was known for being a lazy elf and he was hoping to go home early so that he could have a really nice, long sleep. Ernie wondered
5   what job he would be asked to do. He didn't want to end up with a rubbish task, so if he managed to get to the back of the queue, he thought, then the other elves would have to do the worst jobs and his job would be to help another elf or even to go home early. In fact, if he was slow enough, Santa might not even see him. Ernie cheered up at
10   this thought and when Santa asked for all of the elves to line up, Ernie made sure that he shuffled unhurriedly to the back of the line.

Santa looked around at the elves and then down to his list of jobs. 'Well, my elves', Santa boomed, 'I need three helpers to box up the jigsaws, five elves to package the dolls and teddy bears, six others to put the toy
15   cars into boxes and I need four elves to count the building blocks.'

Ernie was thrilled that he didn't have these jobs to do. He hated boxing up as it required a lot of concentration to count properly and he always ended up with paper cuts.

Santa ticked off the first eighteen elves and off they dashed. Santa
20   looked at the remaining eager faces. 'I now need fifteen helpers to wrap the boxes up in the most Christmassy of wrapping papers.'

Ernie was so relieved that he didn't have to wrap up the presents. This was such a boring job and Ernie usually ended up with more sticky tape on him than on the presents. No, this was not a job that he fancied.

25   Santa ticked off the fifteen elves and looked at the remaining queue. 'Well, my elves, I need two helpers for each reindeer to wash and feed Comet, Cupid, Blitzen, Vixen, Dasher, Dancer, Prancer, Donner and Rudolph.' Santa ticked off each elf as they all trundled off to find their reindeer.

Ernie was ecstatic! He hated washing down the reindeer as he would
30   get soapy and wet and they were such messy eaters that he would end up with hot oats and bits of carrot all over his hands. Ernie shivered. 'What a gross job that is!' he thought. Ernie counted the remaining elves. Including himself there were just fourteen left.

Santa counted the remaining elves. 'Well, my elves, I now need three
35   helpers to polish the sleigh and to make sure that it's ready for the Long

Night. I then need another ten elves to load up all of the boxes into sacks and then onto the sleigh. It is such an important job and needs great care and attention.'

40 The chosen elves giggled, so pleased to be given such an important job. Ernie giggled to himself, glad to be left. Who wants to carry heavy boxes to and fro and being too hot indoors and too cold outdoors? No, this was no job for Ernie. He was above this.

Santa ticked off the remaining job and then turned to find Mrs Claus, when out of the corner of his eye, he saw a movement behind the
45 Christmas tree. 'Ernie. Is that you?' asked Santa.

Ernie scowled. He was so annoyed that he had been spotted.

'Well, Ernie, I have all of my jobs ticked off, so let me think what else needs doing.' Santa rubbed his chin, pulling gently on his long white beard. Then all of a sudden Santa looked at his pocket watch and then
50 turned to Ernie triumphantly. 'Ernie. I know exactly what job would be good for you!'

Ernie looked at Santa, feeling sure that the job would be doing something pointless like tying the ribbons on the dolls' hair or making sure there were batteries in the toys.

55 'Ernie. The reindeer will have eaten by now and need someone to shovel up any mess they have made. They have to feel comfortable before their long travels, so go and grab a shovel, a brush and a bucket and when you have collected all of the reindeer dung, pop it all in the Christmas garden
60 compost heap to give Mrs Claus some lovely roses in the summer.'

Ernie was horrified. To his dismay he had the worst job. In fact, this job was the worst possible job in the whole wide world. Ernie
65 plodded to the stables and looked at the floor. What a mess! Cold oats, bits of carrot, lots of straw and now loads of steaming reindeer dung. Ernie was going to have a very, VERY, **VERY** Long Night.

1 How had Ernie planned to spend the night?

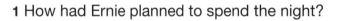

2 What was Ernie's plan to avoid being given a job?

_____

_____

3 Why did Ernie not want to box up presents? Give two reasons.

_____

_____

_____

_____

4 Why did Ernie not want to wrap up presents? Give two reasons.

_____

_____

_____

_____

5 Why did Ernie not want to wash and feed the reindeer? Give two reasons.

_____

_____

_____

_____

6 Why did Ernie not want to clean and pack the sleigh? Give two reasons.

_____

_____

_____

_____

7 How did Santa notice Ernie?

_____

_____

_____

_____

8 What would the reindeer dung be used for?

1 A

_____

_____

_____

1

9 What do these words mean as used in the text? Provide a **definition**.

1 C

a unhurriedly (line 11) _____

b eager (line 20) _____

c dismay (line 62) _____

3

10 Give three ways the author uses the word 'very' in the last **sentence**.

1 F

_____

_____

_____

_____

3

Put these **sentences** in the **past tense** using the smallest number of words possible.

9 mins

4 D

Example   I am eating a sandwich.   _I ate a sandwich_.

11 I am riding my bike.

_____

12 Tomak is swimming in the pool.

_____

13 Megan is speaking to Grandma.

_____

14 Juliet is washing her hair.

_____

15 We are running in the race.

_____

16 Katie is writing in her diary.

_____

6

Take a different **conjunction** from the box and place it in a space so that each **sentence** makes sense.

4 C

although	because	but	if	or	so

17 Joe loves to eat lasagne _____ he doesn't like pizza.

18 Yasmin is not eating lunch _____ she is fasting.

19 Philip was hungry _____ he ate a sandwich.

20 Dad said that I could go out on my bike _____ I could go shopping with him.

21 _____ Connor was angry with his sister, he didn't lose his temper.

22 I can come to your house for a playdate _____ your mum calls mine.

6

Underline the two odd words out in the following groups of words.

15 mins

2 F

Example   purple   lilac   <u>olive</u>   <u>sage</u>   violet

23 Liverpool   France   London   India   Brazil

24 football   basketball   baseball   swimming   diving

25 shirt   scarf   gloves   trousers   hat

26 noun   verb   word   sentence   adverb

27 addition   subtraction   minus   plus   take

5

Write the **singular** version of the words in these **sentences**.

Example   Where is the _____cat_____ ? (cats)

28 Would you like a _____ (glasses) of milk?

29 Hera is the name of a Greek _____ (goddesses).

30 The little _____ (piglets) followed its mother.

31 The _____ (ponies) in the field was chasing another.

32 Is there a _____ (fairies) at the bottom of our garden?

33 There is a _____ (people) looking for Dad.

34 Ben saw a _____ (monkeys) at the zoo.

35 Raj needs a _____ (knives) to cut the bread.

8

Find the three letters that complete these words. The three letters do not have to make a word.

Example   fr**esh** spl**as**h

36 b_____ htest   _____ erwards

37 _____ usand   the_____ lves

38 swim_____ g   butt_____ ly

39 his_____ y   scra_____ g

Underline the one word on the right that has the most opposite meaning to the word on the left.

Example   **rose**   thorn   flower   <u>fell</u>   down   up

40 disappear vanish   go   appear   dissolve   resolve

41 early   first   late   start   stop   dawn

42 **difficult**	impossible	hard	soft	easy	sufficient
43 **regular**	unequal	even	often	level	rough
44 **possible**	likely	probable	potential	unlikely	imaginable
45 **natural**	ordinary	normal	usual	expected	artificial

6

Read the following **sentences** and answer the questions. Underline the correct answer.

3 G

Example   'The plane's departure time was 13:45.'
What does the word 'departure' mean? Answer: **b**

| **a** | **b** | **c** | **d** |
| arriving | <u>leaving</u> | resting | mending |

46 'I need to blend the ice cream with the fruit.'
What does 'blend' mean?

| **a** | **b** | **c** | **d** |
| beat | separate | mix | make |

47 'All pupils need to form a queue behind their class teacher.'
What does 'queue' mean?

| **a** | **b** | **c** | **d** |
| circle | line | choir | group |

48 'Mum wants a career as a teacher.'
What does 'career' mean?

| **a** | **b** | **c** | **d** |
| conversation | meeting | child | job |

49 'We live in the south-east region of the country.'
What does 'region' mean?

| **a** | **b** | **c** | **d** |
| area | county | country | village |

4

Underline the correct words in each of these **sentences**.

Example: She (<u>blew</u>, blue) her trumpet solo in the school (<u>band</u>, banned)

50 There are lots of (poor, pour) countries in the (whirled, world).

51 Sometimes there is a lack of (rain, rein) or too much (son, sun).

52 Sometimes farmers cannot grow enough food, or (their, there) country may (be, bee) at war.

53 In some countries people (die, dye) when their most basic (kneads, needs) are not met.

54 We don't have to (know, no) someone to care (for, four) them.

55 When we (raise, rays) money, we help to (safe, save) the lives of other people.

12

Rearrange these words to make the longest **sentence** you can. Underline the one word that is not needed.

Example: So cream <u>eat</u> the were cakes delicious.
         The cream cakes were so delicious.

56 The hurricane gently bobbed the flowers in pretty breeze.

_____

57 As a lemon our cherry car as new is red.

_____

58 Old Robert working loved museum the at.

_____

59 The two were enemies of best friends the children.

4

Write out the **root word** for each of these words.

Example   unhappiness = happy

60 magically _____

61 beautiful _____

30

Paper 1

1 a teddy bear
2 *any three of the following:* the lines are short, each line begins with a capital letter, there are words that rhyme, the writing is broken into stanzas (verses or sections is acceptable)
3 the camp site, a castle, the beach, a hilltop zoo
4 *any one of the following:* we (wee), sea (see), heard (herd), could (cud), be (bee), waves (waives)
5 Charlie is my favourite friend.
6 *any three of the following:* he makes me laugh, he makes me smile, he always smiles, he is always trying to cheer me up, we laughed so much together, we go everywhere together
7 He is
8 beach, coast
9 narrow, thin, slender
10 team, crowd, mass, pack
11 leave, depart
12 reward, praise
13 huge and big – The other words mean small
14 television and radio – The other words are pinted on paper
15 boiling and hot – The other words mean chilly
16 hand and elbow – The other words are organs
17 driver and passenger – The other words are vehicles
18 bread and cake – The other words are dairy products
19 house
20 church
21 child
22 scarf
23 puppy
24 fly
25 lunch
26 ess (addresses)   pri (princess)
27 ish (punished)   eys (donkeys)
28 won (wonderful)   gin (bringing)
29 che (teachers)   kin (stockings)
30 erh (perhaps)   pul (popular)
31 hem (themselves)
32 tin (writing)
33 low (blowing)
34 had (shadows)
35 din (pudding)
36 rig (brightest)
37 deliberate
38 unsure
39 shrink
40 huge
41 unusual
42 rough

43 c
44 a
45 b
46 a
47 d
48 a
49 c
50 b
51 cinema – There are trapeze artists in a circus.
52 leg – The little dog wagged his tail.
53 bakery – The library had no books about the Vikings.
54 handbag – The queen wore her gold crown.
55 divide – Three add two makes five.
56 teachers – Our classroom has six tables in it.
57 clean
58 poorly
59 warmth
60 large
61 high
62 fashion
63 snip
64 but
65 because
66 or
67 so
68 yet
69 behind
70 through
71 tired
72 morning
73 yawned
74 stretched
75 hungry

Paper 2

1 shape, pattern, decoration
2 safe, harmless
3 yell, scream, howl
4 clean, spotless, sparkling
5 claw, nail
6 feet – You need to wash your hands before making sandwiches.
7 shed – We planted a rose bush in the garden.
8 wood – Jeans are often made from denim.
9 space – The bus to town was running late.
10 coaches – The fishermen returned with full boats.
11 trousers
12 chilly
13 whole
14 divide
15 noise
16 sweep

17 ark (darker)
18 ear (learnt)
19 row (borrowed)
20 the (rather)
21 urn (turnips)
22 ran (strangers)
23 tin (skating)
24 kitten and puppy – The other words are not baby animals
25 fingers and toes – The other words are parts of the face
26 rice and pasta – The other words are things you put food on or in
27 ears and legs – The other words are things you do
28 gold and silver – The other words are types of jewellery
29 fox
30 shop
31 tie
32 box
33 mouse
34 irrelevant
35 part
36 rarely
37 question
38 drop
39 go
40 scarce
41 a
42 e
43 b
44 c
45 c
46 a
47 red (read)
48 plaice (place)
49 new (knew)
50 wear (where)
51 two (to, too)
52 ate (eight)
53 following
54 strawberries
55 apples
56 banana
57 scoops
58 vanilla
59 fruit
60 pals, mates, buddy
61 They have lots of tightly packed teeth making their jaw bones look like a parrot's beak.
62 The mucous layer is brightly coloured.
63 It forms a mucous layer at night to protect it when it is asleep.
64 The goby cleans away the food that is stuck to the teeth of the parrotfish. It gobbles up the rotten skin to keep the parrotfish healthy.
65 'As clean as a new pin.'
66 a eat, chew, gobble, nibble

b stomach, belly
c best, close, tight, strong
67 *Any two of the following:*
They need each other. The parrotfish needs the goby to keep it healthy and clean. The goby needs the parrotfish to provide it with food so that it doesn't have to hunt for food.
68 a
69 c
70 c
71 b
72 ain (rainbow) hic (chicken)
73 und (understood) owe (borrowed)
74 eti (sometimes) din (pudding)
75 ing (darling) rew (firework)

Paper 3

1 He was going to have a long sleep.
2 He was going to be at the very back of the queue.
3 He had to concentrate. He always ended up with paper cuts.
4 It was a boring job. He ended up with sticky tape on him.
5 *Any two of the following:*
He would get soapy and wet. They were messy eaters. He would get hot oats and bits of carrot on his hands.
6 The boxes are heavy. He would feel either too hot or too cold.
7 He was turning to change direction. He spotted a movement behind the Christmas tree.
8 to give Mrs Claus some lovely roses in the summer
9 a slowly
b keen, enthusiastic
c disappointment, panic, alarm
10 *Any three of the following reasons*: the word is repeated twice, two of them are written in block capital letters, one of them is written in bold type, the words get larger
11 I rode my bike.
12 Tomak swam in the pool.
13 Megan spoke to Grandma.
14 Juliet washed her hair.
15 We ran in the race.
16 Katie wrote in her diary.
17 but
18 because
19 so
20 or
21 although
22 if
23 Liverpool and London – The other words are countries

24 swimming and diving – The other words are ball sports
25 shirt and trousers – The other words are outerwear
26 word and sentence – The other words are word classes
27 addition and plus – The other words are to do with taking away
28 glass
29 goddess
30 piglet
31 pony
32 fairy
33 person
34 monkey
35 knife
36 rig (brightest) aft (afterwards)
37 tho (thousand) mse (themselves)
38 min (swimming) erf (butterfly)
39 tor (history) pin (scraping)
40 appear
41 late
42 easy
43 unequal
44 unlikely
45 artificial
46 c mix
47 b line
48 d job
49 a area
50 poor, world
51 rain, sun
52 their, be
53 die, needs
54 know, for
55 raise, save
56 hurricane – The pretty flowers bobbed gently in the breeze.
57 lemon – Our new car is as red as a cherry.
58 old – Robert loved working at the museum.
59 enemies – The two children were the best of friends.
60 magic
61 beauty
62 silly
63 clever
64 small
65 wring (ring)
66 sight (site)
67 hair (hare)
68 their (there, they're)
69 horse (hoarse)
70 break (brake)
71 distance
72 planets
73 remember
74 telescope
75 looking

Paper 4

1 singing
2 forgot
3 baked
4 making
5 contains
6 are
7 owe (however)
8 ass (glasses)
9 ran (branches)
10 tee (thirteen)
11 broken, ruined, wrecked
12 tired, sleepy, dozy, drowsy
13 easy, simple
14 cloth, material
15 carton
16 blaze
17 beast
18 number
19 injury
20 scared
21 unclean
22 fifteen and nineteen – The other words are multiples of ten
23 shape and angle – The other words are types of 2D shapes
24 leaves and snow – The other words are seasons
25 one and single – The other words are types of twos
26 fleece and jacket – The other words are fastenings
27 ldi (building) ure (pictured)
28 bec (because) ado (shadowed)
29 ies (heaviest) pin (slipping)
30 red (hundred) our (fourteen)
31 iti (writing) bir (birthday)
32 bright
33 steps
34 ring
35 hard
36 mean
37 a shut
38 c nice
39 c white
40 b price
41 owl, food
42 looked, screeching
43 little, tasty
44 carefully, loudly
45 cushion
46 purse
47 thief
48 party
49 child
50 Alice thought about her new rabbit.
51 George bought a book for school.
52 Rose went to visit her cousin. *OR* Rose visited her cousin.
53 Elijah brought his friend to the party.

54 Brooke had a friendly teacher.
55 Dolores was tired.
56 Michael slept at Mimi's house.
57 sit
58 travel
59 possible
60 act
61 settle
62 breakfast
63 prefers
64 usually
65 porridge
66 dried
67 fruit
68 d
69 c
70 d, e
71 b, d
72 d
73 c
74 a pile
   b colourful
   c restoring
75 b

Paper 5

1 because otherwise people would not know which king or queen we mean
2 Henry II
3 1455
4 Henry VI
5 12 years old
6 Lady Jane Grey
7 5 years
8 the Tudors / 1485–1603
9 House of Hanoverians / 1714–1901
10 Queen Victoria
11 Queen Anne died without leaving any children. The German George I was her closest Protestant relative.
12 There was anti-German feeling because of the First World War, and Windsor sounded more English.
13 loss, defeat
14 build, make, create
15 open, expose
16 fear, dread, horror, fright
17 mild, kind, soft
18 bored (board)
19 you (ewe, yew)
20 him (hymn)
21 weight (wait)
22 flower (flour)
23 cottage and house – The other words are settlements
24 forest and woods – The other words are flowers
25 butterfly and moth – The other words are minibeasts who cannot fly

26 nostrils and lips – The other words are parts of the eye
27 ybi (ladybird)   ict (dictionary)
28 aug (naughty)   ter (literacy)
29 cro (crowded)   eri (showering)
30 ass (assembly)   ona (lemonade)
31 fin (finishing)
32 eve (thieves)
33 ten (fastening)
34 oat (floated)
35 ash (splashed)
36 all (shallow)
37 pea (speaking)
38 century
39 built
40 history
41 library
42 special
43 leave
44 doubt
45 old
46 similar
47 bored
48 begin
49 *any two of the following*: classroom, teacher, lesson
50 slipped, taught
51 upstairs, French
52 quietly, thoroughly
53 she, his
54 top
55 wind
56 train
57 minute
58 spring
59 Joy bent the straw.
60 Jack drank water.
61 Rod hid in the garden.
62 Ravi lay in bed.
63 We shook hands with everyone.
64 Tranmere Rovers won the match.
65 Mai Mai wound the clock up.
66 lived
67 animals
68 squirrel
69 finding
70 hopped
71 twitching
72 vixen
73 hunted
74 emerged
75 undergrowth

Paper 6

1 a sunset
   b perfume
2 a jumped
   b unknowing

3 a ongoing
   b stopping
4 reign, rule, govern
5 unusual, different, odd, strange
6 undecided, unsure
7 caught, trapped
8 mane (main)   paws (pause)
9 weigh (way)   lead (led)
10 fought (fort)   bold (bowled)
11 meet (meat)   tire (tyre)
12 beat (beet)   tacks (tax)
13 night (knight)   for (fore, four)
14 cow – The owl hooted in the forest.
15 eating – We were acting in the play.
16 slept – We clapped at the end of the performance.
17 custard – They ate vegetables with the noodles.
18 town – We parked our car in the car park.
19 butterflies – Hundreds of frogspawn developed into tadpoles.
20 Tipsy
21 Topsy
22 Dipsy
23 Flopsy
24 pad (spades)
25 vat (private)
26 pot (spotted)
27 ask (basket)
28 ten (mittens)
29 pig (pigeons)
30 and (handbag)
31 ball
32 pen
33 stick
34 sweet
35 tablet
36 upset
37 weakness
38 follow
39 teach
40 straight
41 build
42 remember
43 freezing
44 Bella draws a picture. *OR* Bella is drawing a picture.
45 Simon climbs the ladder. *OR* Simon is climbing the ladder.
46 The dog sleeps in his basket. *OR* The dog is sleeping in his basket.
47 Kayleigh drives the tractor. *OR* Kayleigh is driving the tractor.
48 Erica flies a kite. *OR* Erica is flying a kite.
49 peaceful
50 quiet
51 themselves
52 coloured
53 insects
54 actually

55 habitat
56 nature
57 clothed
58 middle
59 idea
60 own
61 maybe
62 so
63 because
64 and
65 but
66 or

67 In a magazine or comic plus *any three of the following*: the writing in in text boxes, there are lots of facts and figures, there is an interview, the text refers to readers, it refers to a weekly edition, it says that you can buy the edition from a newsagents
68 Ginger biscuits would be made on 19th May.
69 occasion cakes
70 15th July

71 Sammy Jacobson
72 Harder fruit takes longer to cook than softer fruit.
73 225 g of butter is needed (25 g in the filling + 200 g in the topping)
74 a rough
   b contestants
   c version
75 fling, chuck, toss, pop

62 silliness _____

63 cleverest _____

64 smaller _____

A **homophone** is a word that sounds like another word but has a different spelling. Underline the one **homophone** in each line.

Example   wish   <u>war</u>   when   wicket   welcome   (war and wore)

65 wring   squeeze   twist   spin   rotate

66 view   sight   vision   spot   picture

67 beard   moustache   brush   hair   extensions

68 them   those   think   their   thought

69 sheep   horse   donkey   cow   goat

70 break   holiday   vacation   trip   escape

71–75 Put the words in the box into the correct places in the paragraph below.

distance	looking	planets	remember	telescope

There are eight planets in our solar system. In order of _____

from the sun, the _____ are Mercury, Venus, Earth, Mars,

Jupiter, Saturn, Uranus and Neptune. I use this sentence to _____

the order of them: **M**y **V**ery **E**arly **M**orning **J**og **S**hould **U**pset **N**obody.
All of these planets can be seen with binoculars or a

_____ and some can even be seen just by

_____ up to the sky.

Paper 4

Underline the correct word in each of these **sentences**.

Example   Jon (was /<u>is</u>) going to play golf tomorrow.

1 Chrissy and her friend enjoy (singing/sang) in the school choir.

2 Nicki (forget/forgot) her words in assembly.

3 Roshana (bake/baked) a cake for Solomon's birthday.

4 Dad will be (made/making) a volcano for my school project.

5 This book (contain/contains) lots of questions.

6 Where (are/is) my blue shoes?

Find the three-letter word that can be added to the letters in capitals to make a new word. The new word will complete the **sentence** sensibly.

Example   We HED the keys to the estate agent.   <u>AND</u>

7 HVER you travel, leave plenty of time to get here. _____

8 The optician has given me some GLES to correct my sight.

_____

9 The BCHES of the tree needed pruning. _____

10 Some people think that THIRN is unlucky. _____

Look at the following words and then use them to answer the questions that follow.

weak	dull	drowsy	wrecked	purse
cloth	stool	change	watch	broken
order	wise	simple	sleepy	chew
tied	ruined	roam	sure	paid
dozy	tired	sore	easy	material

11 Find three words that are **synonyms** for the word 'destroyed'.

2 A

_____

_____

12 Find four words that are **antonyms** for the word 'awake'.

2 B

_____

_____

13 Find two words that are **antonyms** for the word 'difficult'.

2 B

_____

14 Find two words that are **synonyms** for the word 'fabric'.

2 A

_____

11

10 mins

Add the missing letters to the word on the right to make a word with the most similar meaning to the word on the left.

2C 3C

Example: vision   s _i_ _g_ h t

15 container   c _ _ _ t _ n

16 fire   b l a _ _ _

17 creature   _ _ a s t

18 amount   n _ _ _ e r

19 damage   i n _ _ _ y

20 afraid   s c a _ _ _

21 dirty   u _ _ _ _ a n

7

Underline the two odd words out in the following groups of words.

2 F

Example   purple   lilac   <u>olive</u>   <u>sage</u>   violet

22 twenty   fifteen   thirty   nineteen   sixty

23 pentagon   shape   angle   octagon   hexagon

33

24 autumn	leaves	winter	snow	summer
25 couple	one	pair	double	single
26 button	zip	fleece	jacket	laces

5

Find the three letters that complete these words. The three letters do not have to make a word.

3 B

Example   fr<u>esh</u> sp<u>las</u>h

27 bui_____ ng   pict_____ d

28 _____ ause   sh_____ wed

29 heav_____ t   slip_____ g

30 hund_____   f_____ teen

31 wr_____ ng   _____ thday

5

Underline the one word in brackets that goes equally well with both pairs of words.

2 E

Example   chilly, breezy   trendy, fashionable   (cold, <u>cool,</u> warm, hot, chic)

32 clever, brainy   light, shining   (dull, dim, bright, intelligent, gleaming)

33 walks, paces   stairs, ladders   (rambles, rope, plods, steps, marches)

34 call, telephone   circle, loop   (ring, buzz, disk, shout, doughnut)

35 rigid, strong   difficult, tough   (taut, inflexible, stiff, firm, hard)

36 cruel, nasty   stingy, miserly   (kind, lovely, mean, bad, nice)

5

Read the following **sentences** and answer the questions. Underline the correct answer.

Example 'The plane's departure time was 13:45.'
What does the word 'departure' mean? Answer: **b**

a	b	c	d
arriving	<u>leaving</u>	resting	mending

37 'We are going to close the shop on a Wednesday.'
What does 'close' mean?

a	b	c	d
shut	empty	nearby	front

38 'The weather last night was very pleasant.'
What does 'pleasant' mean?

a	b	c	d
rainy	funny	nice	stormy

39 'After the shock of the accident she looked really pale.'
What does 'pale' mean?

a	b	c	d
sad	happy	white	dark

40 'Why is the cost of that book so high?'
What does 'cost' mean?

a	b	c	d
sale	price	tax	money

4

Read the following **sentence** and then find two examples of each word class to complete the table below.

15 mins

The little owl looked carefully at the tasty food before screeching loudly.

41	**noun**		
42	**verb**		
43	**adjective**		
44	**adverb**		

8

Write the **singular** version of the words in these **sentences**.

Example   Where is the _____cat_____ ? (cats)

45 Mum placed the _____ (cushions) on the bed.

46 There was no money left in Mina's _____ (purses).

47 The _____ (thieves) stole the boy's scooter.

48 We had a _____ (parties) to celebrate Grandpa's birthday.

49 Our _____ (children) is really good at drawing horses.

5

Put these **sentences** in the **past tense**, using the smallest number of words possible.

Example   I am eating a sandwich.   <u>I ate a sandwich.</u>

50 Alice is thinking about her new rabbit.

_____

51 George is buying a book for school.

_____

52 Rose is going to visit her cousin.

_____

53 Elijah is bringing his friend to the party.

_____

54 Brooke has a friendly teacher.

_____

55 Dolores will be tired.

_____

56 Michael is sleeping at Mimi's house.

_____

7

Write out the **root word** for each of these words.

Example   unhappiness = happy

57 resitting   ————————————

58 travelling   ————————————

59 impossibly   ————————————

60 inactive   ————————————

61 unsettled   ————————————

○ 5

62–67 The underlined words in this paragraph have not been spelled correctly. Write out the misspelled words in the right-hand box, so that the spellings are correct and the paragraph makes sense. The first word has been done for you.

Eleanor loves to eat <u>serial</u> for	e.g. cereal
<u>breckfast</u>, but her little sister Lil	**62**
<u>prefurs</u> eggs or peanut butter on	
toast. Their big sister Jessica <u>useuly</u>	**63**
picks a huge bowl of <u>porigge</u> with	**64**
<u>dride</u> fruit and honey, although Mum	**65**
likes ham and cheese with fresh <u>frute</u>.	
All of them drink a small glass of fruit	**66**
smoothie and a big glass of milk.	**67**

○ 6

Read the following comprehension text and answer the questions that follow it.

The Old and the New

'Where's Al?' Dad called as he came downstairs carrying a cardboard box. 'Look, I've found a whole stash of really old comics in the attic,' he continued as he placed the box on the table. Al lifted the lid of the box to reveal a dazzling comic with paper as fragile as tissue. He wasn't
5   keen on reading books, but comics were another matter.

Al had sat flicking through the comics, mainly *Boys Only Paper*, which contained stories and articles, when he came across a long brown envelope. The envelope had already been opened, and Al was surprised to see his address written on the front. He peered in and took out a wad

10 of thin paper filled with spidery writing. Al soon realised, with growing excitement, that he was looking at a beautifully written letter. 'Dad – listen to this,' Al said as he began reading out: 'Rosebud Cottage, Daisy Bank, Worcestershire.' Dad sat down at the table and began to listen to Al. 'To my dearest Cecily, I am so awfully thrilled that you were able to

15 visit last Saturday. We had such a wonderful time in the gardens and I hope that it will not be long before you are able to visit again. Next time I should love to find the sunken garden that must be on the other side of the door. Nanny says that if we walk across Bluebell Field to the corner of Smestow Farm, we should be able to reach the back of the sunken

20 garden, so we could try this.'

Al looked at his father questioningly. 'Where is Bluebell Field or Smestow Farm or Daisy Bank? They all sound so pretty.' Dad shrugged. 'I don't know, son. I'm still trying to get my bearings.'

Al looked back at the letter. 'Jeffrey is renovating the orangery, and the

25 rosebeds are now looking rather marvellous. Although it is only early June, the heady smell of honeysuckle fills the evening air and the lilac tree looks delightful. I do so wish that you could be here at the moment. It is the most beautiful place in the whole world. Please ask your mama if you can ride here at the weekend and until then, toodle pip, your

30 loving friend Gladys.'

Al looked through the French doors at his new garden. 'Dad, can we have a sunken garden?' Dad laughed. 'Al – I don't really know what one is, but you've only just got enough garden to kick the football about. Do you really want to give that up?' Al looked back to the cardboard box

35 and top of the pile was an old map of Worcestershire. Al reasoned that if Cecily could ride to this beautiful garden, it couldn't be that far away. He opened the map and poured over it.

'What have you got there?' Dad asked.

'It's just an old map,' replied Al, 'but I can't find any gardens on it.'

40 'Let's have a look', Dad said. 'Can you see the farm on there?' He took the map from Al and within a few minutes, he had found not only Smestow Farm, but also Bluebell Field and Daisy Bank. Dad laughed again, 'Al, I don't think this is really a garden as such. If it is large enough to be named on this map, I think it is more like a park!' Al was

45 so excited. 'Please Dad, can we go and find it? It isn't far away, is it?'

Dad looked at his watch. 'No, it isn't far and I suppose we could have a quick drive up there now, before we finish unpacking. I must admit I am more than ready to escape from these boxes.'

Al sat in the back of the car, feeling so excited. He could almost smell

50 the roses and honeysuckle. He could picture the lilac tree and he was desperate to know what an orangery and a sunken garden looked like. He wondered whether he would find the garden and whether it still looked the same. Maybe now it had changed and it was a park for everyone to enjoy. Al wasn't so sure about sharing the garden with

55 everyone else, but even if it was now a park, he had something special as he had the letter.

Dad followed the little lanes cutting through the farmland until he reached a more builtup area. Dad frowned and checked the map. 'It's straight on here,' he said, continuing through the traffic lights.

60 More houses and shops gradually appeared alongside the road. Al saw churches, schools, a post office, another row of shops, some offices and a multi-storey car park. Dad turned into another road even bigger than before, in an area that should have been the crossroads of Smestow Farm and Bluebell Field. Al looked in shock at what he saw.

65 There were no roses, no honeysuckle, no lilac tree, no sunken garden and nothing that looked remotely like an orangery. Before him, and sprawling back as far as he could see, were the familiar names of a retail park. The huge supermarket, the shoe warehouse, the fast food drive-through restaurants and a massive cinema stood next to a giant

70 clothes shop, a rambling range of well-known shops and the huge neon sign that declared, 'Bluebell Retail Park.'

Underline the correct letter (or letters).

68 Where was the letter?

   a on the table

   b on the top of the cardboard box

   c inside a book

   d in the middle of the pile of comics

69 Who lived at Rosebud Cottage?

  a Al

  b Cecily

  c Gladys

  d Jeffrey

70 What two reasons did Dad give for not creating a sunken garden?

  a It would be too expensive.

  b It would take a long time to build.

  c Dad hadn't got his bearings yet.

  d There was not enough space.

  e Al wouldn't be able to play football.

71 What two reasons did Dad give for agreeing to look for the garden?

  a It would be large enough to be like a park.

  b Dad wanted a rest from unpacking.

  c Dad wanted to get his bearings.

  d It was quite close by.

  e Dad wanted to do some shopping.

72 How do you think Al felt when they arrived at their destination?

  a excited

  b relieved

  c happy

  d upset

73 Why do you think Al felt like this?

  a He loved retail parks.

  b He hated shopping.

  c He was expecting flowers and trees.

  d There was a massive cinema.

74 What do the words on the left mean as used in the text? Underline the answer.

a stash	bag	pile	parcel	chest
b dazzling	delicate	old	tough	colourful
c renovating	restoring	building	destroying	painting

40

75 How do you think Al would have felt if he had found the garden was an open park?

    a pleased so that other people could enjoy it

    b jealous as he didn't want to share the garden

    c angry as he didn't want the garden to look different

    d excited as he would love to tell people about his letter

Now go to the Progress Chart to record your score!   **Total**   90

Paper 5

Read the following comprehension text and answer the questions that follow it.

The Kings and Queens of England

Normans (1066–1154)

When William the Conqueror (William I) won the Battle of Hastings in 1066, he became the first Norman king. After William, the country was then ruled by William II, Henry I, Stephen and finally Matilda. We place
5　the roman numerals after each king or queen to mean William the first or William the second, otherwise people would not know which William or which Henry we mean. There are still Norman building styles in England and the Normans also gave us their language.

Plantagenets (1154–1399)

10　King Henry II was the first of the Plantagenet kings followed by Richard I, John I, Henry III, Edward I, Edward II, Edward III and Richard II. The Plantagenet kings gave us a parliament, some very violent wars abroad and fighting in England while Wales was conquered.

House of Lancaster (1399–1461)

15　Henry IV took the throne from Richard II to begin the dynasty we refer to as the House of Lancaster. After Henry IV, Henry V and Henry VI ruled. Henry VI was only nine months old when he became king, but he remained king until he was in his thirties. In 1455, the famous 'Wars of the Roses' began between the houses of Lancaster
20　and York.

House of York (1461–1485)

King Edward IV was the first king from the house of York. He was followed by Edward V and Richard III. When Edward IV died, the crown passed to Edward V who was only 12, but he ended up as one of the
25　young princes who were locked in the Tower of London and never seen again. Richard then became heir to the crown although most people suspect that he was involved in the deaths of the two young princes.

The Tudors (1485–1603)

Richard III died in battle and Henry VII took the crown. After Henry VII,
30　England was ruled by Henry VIII, Edward VI, Lady Jane Grey, Queen Mary I and finally Elizabeth I. During the Tudor period, England became a huge colonial power. During this time, Wales and England were united

through an Act of Union. Henry VIII was well known for his many wives, whereas Lady Jane Grey was only queen for 9 days and was beheaded when she was only 17.

The Stuarts (1603–1649 then 1660–1714)

James I was the first of our Stuart kings. He was followed by Charles I, Charles II, James II, William III, Mary II and Anne. In 1649, King Charles I was killed and England was left without a King. Instead no monarch ruled, although Oliver Cromwell took charge between 1653 and 1658. Charles II took over in 1660 to continue the Stuart period. In 1707, England and Scotland were united by another Act of Union.

House of Hanover (1714–1901)

King George I was the first Hanoverian King of England. He was followed by George II, George III, George IV, William IV and Queen Victoria. This was a German line of monarchs who ruled us after Queen Anne had died without leaving any children. King George was her closest Protestant relative. During this period of time, another Act of Union united Great Britain with Ireland.

Saxe-Coburg-Gotha and the Windsors (1901–present day)

King Edward VII was the first king after Queen Victoria. After him, the United Kingdom was ruled by George V, Edward VIII, George VI and Elizabeth II. When George V took to the throne, there was a lot of anti-German feeling because of the First World War, so he changed the family name to Windsor.

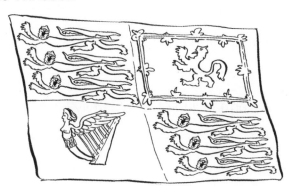

1 Why do we use the Roman numerals after each king or queen?

_____

_____

_____

_____

2 Who was the first Plantagenet king?

_____ ○1

3 When did the Wars of the Roses begin?

_____ ○1

4 Who was the last king of the House of Lancaster?

_____ ○1

5 How old was Edward V when he was made king?

_____ ○1

6 Who was beheaded at the age of 17?

_____ ○1

7 For how long did Oliver Cromwell rule?

_____ ○1

8 In what period of time was the first Act of Union?

_____ ○1

9 In what period of time was Great Britain united with Ireland?

_____ ○1

10 Who was the last Hanoverian monarch?

_____ ○1

11 Why were we ruled by a German line of royal family?

[1 B]

_____

_____

_____ ○2

12 Why did the Saxe-Coburg-Gotha change their name to Windsor?

[1 B]

_____

_____

_____ ○1

Look at the following words and then use them to answer the questions that follow.

taste	kind	open	loss	expose
build	arch	shut	meal	fright
dread	trying	defeat	flame	make
spy	fear	frog	create	hammer
soft	horror	band	flying	mild

13 Find two words that are **antonyms** for the word 'win'.

_____

14 Find three words that are **antonyms** for the word 'destroy'.

_____

_____

15 Find two words that are **antonyms** for the word 'close'.

_____

16 Find four words that are **synonyms** for the word 'terror'.

_____

_____

17 Find three words that are **synonyms** for the word 'gentle'.

_____

_____

A **homophone** is a word that sounds like another word but has a different spelling. Underline the one **homophone** in each line.

Example   wish   <u>war</u>   when   wicket   welcome   (war and wore)

18 excited   challenged   interested   engaged   bored

19 you   me   us   them   her

20	him	she	his	this	it
21	height	weight	length	breadth	width
22	tree	shrub	flower	bulb	plant

5

Underline the two odd words out in the following groups of words.

2 F

Example   purple   lilac   <u>olive</u>   <u>sage</u>   violet

23	cottage	town	village	city	house
24	forest	woods	poppy	daisy	sunflower
25	snail	butterfly	worm	moth	slug
26	nostrils	brows	lips	lashes	lids

4

Find the three letters that complete these words. The three letters do not have to make a word.

3 B

Example   fr**esh** spl**as**h

27 lad_____ rd   d_____ ionary

28 n_____ hty   li_____ acy

29 _____ wded   show_____ ng

30 _____ embly   lem_____ de

4

Find the three-letter word that can be added to letters in capitals to make a new word. The new word will complete the **sentence** sensibly.

3 A

Example   We HED the keys to the estate agent.   <u>AND</u>

31 Joy was first across the ISHING line in the race. _____

32 The THIS stole the money from the bank. _____

33 The park keeper was FASING the gates with a padlock. _____

34 The pieces of bread FLED on the water until the ducks ate it. _____

35 We put on our wellies and SPLED in the puddles. _____

36 We like to swim in the SHOW water. _____

37 We were SKING to the teacher at parents' evening. _____

38–42 The underlined words in this paragraph have not been spelled correctly. Write out the misspelled words in the right-hand box, so that the spellings are correct and the paragraph makes sense. The first word has been done for you.

In <u>Febuary</u> it will be a <u>century</u> since our school was <u>bilt</u>. We want to make the <u>histery</u> of our school available for everyone to read about, so we have extended the school <u>libary</u>. Now anyone can come in and find out more and to help us celebrate our <u>speshul</u> occasion.	e.g. February 38 39 40 41 42

Underline the one word on the right that has the most opposite meaning to the word on the left.

Example   rose   thorn   flower   <u>fell</u>   down   up

43 arrive   leave   come   entrance   part   entry

44 believe   trust   faith   doubt   certainly   hope

45 fresh   latest   new   current   old   near

46 opposite   parallel   near   antonym   similar   apart

47 interested   engaged   fun   absorbed   special   bored

48 end   finish   conclude   begin   continue   partial

Read the following **sentence** and then find two examples of each word class to complete the table below.

She quietly slipped into the upstairs classroom as the French teacher thoroughly taught his lesson.

49	noun		
50	verb		
51	adjective		
52	adverb		
53	pronoun		

10

Underline the one word in brackets that goes equally well with both pairs of words.

12 mins

2 E

Example   chilly, breezy   trendy, fashionable   (cold, <u>cool,</u> warm, hot, chic)

54 shirt, blouse   lid, cap   (jacket, outer, top, bottle, pop)

55 breeze, blowy   twist, turn   (wind, gale, storm, key, rotate)

56 teach, coach   plane, taxi   (car, tank, train, tutor, cab)

57 second, hour   tiny, little   (day, week, time, minute, dinky)

58 leap, jump   summer, winter   (bounce, autumn, spring, season, hop)

5

Put these **sentences** in the **past tense** using the smallest number of words possible.

4 D

Example   I am eating a sandwich.   <u>I ate a sandwich</u>.

59 Joy is bending the straw.

_____

60 Jack is drinking water.

_____

61 Rob is hiding in the garden.

_____

62 Ravi is lying in bed.

_____

63 We have to shake hands with everyone.

_____

64 Tranmere Rovers are winning the match.

_____

65 Mai Mai is winding the clock up.

_____ 7

66–75 Put the words in the box into the correct place in the paragraph below. 3 F

| animals | emerged | finding | hopped | hunted |
| lived | squirrel | twitching | undergrowth | vixen |

In the woods there _____ many _____ such

as the grey _____ , who spent each day busily rushing around

_____ nuts from the trees then burying the nuts here and there.

The rabbits _____ about _____ their whiskers as

they played. At night, the nocturnal animals came out. The _____

and her baby fox cubs _____ for food as the black and white

badgers _____ from their sett snuffling and stomping in the

_____ . 10

Paper 6

Read the following **sentences** and answer the questions. Underline the correct answer.

Example 'The plane's departure time was 13:45.'
What does the word 'departure' mean? Answer: **b**

a	b	c	d
arriving	<u>leaving</u>	resting	mending

1 'At dusk the scent of the honeysuckle was at its sweetest.'

a What does the word 'dusk' mean?

a	b	c	d
dawn	noon	sunset	midnight

b What does the word 'scent' mean?

a	b	c	d
perfume	colour	growth	flowers

2 'The stoat danced and leapt to hypnotise the unsuspecting hare.'

a What does the word 'leapt' mean?

a	b	c	d
turned	ran	jumped	stared

b What does the word 'unsuspecting' mean?

a	b	c	d
shy	stationary	entertained	unknowing

3 'The war was continuing with no sign of ceasing from either side.'

a What does the word 'continuing' mean?

a	b	c	d
fierce	slowing	ongoing	fighting

b What does the word 'ceasing' mean?

a	b	c	d
stopping	pinching	persisting	remaining

3

Look at the following words and then use them to answer the questions that follow.

different	learn	notice	experience	unusual
favourite	strange	trust	island	best
reign	continue	surprise	appear	trapped
considered	undecided	purpose	reveal	unsure
caught	rule	thought	odd	govern

4 Find three words that are **synonyms** for the word 'control'.

_____

_____

5 Find four words that are **antonyms** for the word 'ordinary'.

_____

_____

6 Find two words that are **synonyms** for the word 'uncertain'.

_____

7 Find two words that are **antonyms** for the word 'free'.

_____

A **homophone** is a word that sounds like another word but has a different spelling. Underline the two **homophones** in each line.

Example   car   <u>war</u>   <u>bar</u>   far   jar
           (war and wore; bar and barre)

8 foot	coat	mane	saddle	paws
9 weigh	lead	go	scales	heavy
10 fought	bold	brave	hero	fight
11 fetch	meet	sleep	tire	bed
12 rhythm	music	beat	drum	tacks
13 night	day	for	against	with

51

Rearrange these words to make the longest **sentence** you can. Underline the one word that is not needed.

Example   So cream <u>eat</u> the were cakes delicious.
                The cream cakes were so delicious.

14 The cow forest hooted in the owl.

_____

15 Eating play acting the we in were.

_____

16 The performance slept end clapped we at of the.

_____

17 Noodles with the custard they ate vegetables.

_____

18 In our town car we parked the car park.

_____

19 Hundreds of tadpoles butterflies frogspawn developed into.

_____

6

Read the following paragraph and then answer the questions that follow.

Four little kittens are very playful. Topsy has a red collar and white paws, and her sister Flopsy has a blue collar and black paws. The youngest kitten, Tipsy, has black paws and a red collar and the oldest kitten, Dipsy, has the same colour paws as Topsy and the same coloured collar as Flopsy.

20 Which kitten has a red collar and black paws?

_____

21 Which kitten has a red collar and white paws?

_____

22 Which kitten has a blue collar and white paws?

_____

23 Which kitten has a blue collar and black paws?

_____

4

Find the three-letter word that can be added to the letters in capitals to make a new word. The new word will complete the **sentence** sensibly.

Example   We HED the keys to the estate agent.   <u>AND</u>

24 The gardener was cleaning her forks and SES. _____

25 We couldn't go through the door as it had 'PRIE' on it.

_____

26 The rare eagle was STED by the bird watcher. _____

27 We placed the strawberries into the BET. _____

28 Herrmann put the MITS on to keep his hands warm. _____

29 Please don't feed the EONS that flock into the city centre.

_____

30 Mum put on her coat and picked up her HBAG. _____

Underline the one word in brackets that goes equally well with both pairs of words.

15 mins.

Example   chilly, breezy   trendy, fashionable   (cold, <u>cool,</u> warm, hot, chic)

31 bat, wickets   party, prom   (racquet, ball, jig, stake, owl)

32 coop, hutch   pencil, crayon   (kennel, shed, barn, pen, paint)

33 glue, attach   pole, rod   (paste, stick, beam, connect, post)

34 cute, adorable   dessert, pudding   (lovely, sweet, kind, poppet, dinky)

35 pill, medicine   laptop, notebook   (tablet, lotion, computer, smart, pop)

36 overturn, spill   tearful, weepy   (knock, hurt, cry, upset, mean)

Add the missing letters to the word on the right to make a word with the most opposite meaning to the word on the left.

Example   take   g <u>i</u> <u>v</u> e

37 strength   w e a __ __ __ __ s

38 lead   f __ __ l o w

39 learn   t e __ __ __

40 wobbly   __ __ __ a i g h t

41 destroy   __ u i l __

42 forget   r __ m __ m __ e __

43 boiling   f r e __ __ __ __ g

Put the following **sentences** in the **present tense**.

Example   Sammy toasted a sandwich.   <u>*Sammy toasts a sandwich.*</u>

44 Bella drew a picture.

_____

45 Simon climbed the ladder.

_____

46 The dog slept in his basket.

_____

47 Kayleigh drove the tractor.

_____

48 Erica flew a kite.

_____

49–56 The underlined words in this paragraph have not been spelled correctly. Write out the misspelled words in the right-hand box, so that the spellings are correct and the paragraph makes sense. The first word has been done for you.

The <u>cannall</u> seems such a <u>peacfull</u> place doesn't it? Yet if you sit beside the water and keep <u>queite</u> and still, you would certainly change your mind. Little water rats zoom here and there, water voles and tiny shrews busy <u>themselevs</u> as vivid <u>colord</u> kingfishers fly to and from their nest. Ducks, swans and a whole host of <u>insexts</u> live off the water. A canal is <u>actuly</u> a very busy <u>habbittatt</u> and a wonderful place for <u>naychur</u> to thrive.	e.g. canal 49 50 51 52 53 54 55 56

8

Underline the one word on the right that has the most similar meaning to the word on the left.

Example   **rose**   thorn   flower   <u>ascended</u> down   up

57 dressed   talked   home   residence   clothed   wardrobe

58 centre   shape   circle   edge   middle   side

59 thought   idea   brain   spoke   knew   ignorance

60 possess   danger   prohibit   stop   own   pay

61 probably   impossible   definitely   maybe   never   always

5

Take a different **conjunction** from the box and place it in a space so that each **sentence** makes sense.

and	*because*	*but*	*or*	*so*

62 Lewis wanted to play ice hockey _____ he joined the local team.

63 Sam and Spencer had a sleepover _____ it was the weekend.

64 Mum makes lovely callaloo _____ she cooks delicious pelau.

65 Grace prefers dogs _____ Emily prefers cats.

66 Next year, we will go on holiday to France_____ we might go to Spain.

5

Read the following comprehension text and then answer the questions that follow it.

The Great Under-12 Cook Off Show

Here at the *Great Under-12 Cook Off Show*, we're excited about the new series. There are twelve programmes in the series that we will be treated to. Here is the full series so that you don't miss any of your favourites.

5th May	Cakes	From coffee to toffee – all of our favourite big cakes.
12th May	Bakes	Little cakes, flapjacks and lunchbox favourites.
19th May	Biscuits & Cookies	Spiced, iced, savoury and sweet biscuits.
26th May	Breads	Rolls, batches, baps and loaves.
2nd June	Scones	Sweet, savoury and drop scones.
9th June	Muffins	From healthy breakfast muffins to cupcakes and fairy cakes.
16th June	Occasions	Weddings, birthdays and all manner of decorated cakes.
23th June	Tarts & Pies	From tiny jam tarts to huge tarte tatins, this will test our bakers.
1st July	Puddings	Sponges, steamed puddings and fruit crumbles.
8th July	Quarter-Final	How will the quarter-finalists impress us this week?
15th July	Semi-Final	This will be a week for show-stopping, impressive cakes.
22nd July	Grand Final	Our winner is announced and awarded a £10,000 prize.

To kick off the show, we're going to share some top tips and a winning recipe from last year's winner, Sammy Jacobson, interviewed by Tope Oyeyemi.

'Hey Sammy – it's been nearly a year since your win, so how was your year?'

'I cannot tell you how exciting it was to take part and then to win. It has been a mad year as I have been in school during the week and then at the weekend, I've been doing cookery demonstrations and writing my first cookery book aimed at children.'

'Wow, Sammy, that sounds so busy! Would you recommend our readers take part in the competition?'

'I know that filming has finished for this year, but they will soon be looking for new participants, so sign up and take part because it will change your life. It was the best thing that I have ever done.'

'Finally Sammy, can you give us a tasty recipe out of your new book?'

'Of course! Here is my recipe for easy autumn crumble with a healthy twist and a top tip.'

'Many thanks, Sammy, and we'll all be cheering on this year's contestants!'

Next week Tope Oyeyemi will be interviewing Cupcake Queen Kaitlin O'Donnell with some ideas on how to decorate your cupcakes so that they look professional.

Sammy's Super Sweet

Ingredients for the filling:
500 g autumn fruit such as apples, plums, pears, blackberries (either one fruit or mixed)
75 g sugar
25 g butter
$\frac{1}{4}$ teaspoon of mixed spice or cinnamon (if you fancy it; if not, miss it out)
$\frac{1}{4}$ teaspoon of dried chilli – (I know it sounds mad, but trust me, it works perfectly)

Ingredients for the crumble topping:
100 g plain flour
250 g porridge oats (coarse, fine, a mixture of the two – it doesn't matter)
200 g butter, cut into chunks
180 g brown sugar (white if you don't have brown)

Method:

Preheat the oven to 180°C/Gas Mark 4.

1 Throw all of the filling ingredients into a saucepan and heat through gently until the fruit is soft enough to place a fork through it. Apples are dense and will take 10 minutes, but softer fruit like plums will only take 2 minutes.

2 Fling all of the crumble topping ingredients into a clean bowl and use a fork to stir it all up together and to spread the butter throughout the topping.

3 Chuck the fruit mix into your oven-proof bowl.

4 Toss the crumble topping on top of the fruit and pop it in the oven for 45 minutes.

5 Serve with custard, cream or ice cream.

Top Tip!
You can make up loads of crumble topping, pop it in a freezer bag and freeze it. It will stay in chunks so it is easy to use. For a quick pud, grab a tin of fruit and put it in an oven-proof bowl, then tip over a few generous handfuls of crumble topping and bake.

Next week's edition comes with a free guide to making sugar paste roses.
Out on Monday from all good newsagents.

---

67 Where would you expect to find this text? Can you find three things to back up your point of view?

_____

_____

_____

_____

_____

68 What date do you think you could see a ginger biscuit being made?

_____

69 What will be made on the 16th June?

_____

70 What will be the date of the semi-final?

_____

71 What was the name of last year's winner of the *Under-12 Cook Off Show*?

1 A

_____

72 Why does the fruit take different times to cook?

_____

73 How much butter do you need in total to make the recipe?

_____

74 What do the words on the left mean as used in the text? Underline the answer.

a coarse	rough	soft	rude	smooth	flat
b participants	readers	writers	contestants	eaters	children
c twist	spiral	leap	version	plait	bunch

75 Reread the 'Method' section of the recipe. The word 'throw' is informal. Can you find another four informal words in this section?

_____

_____

_____

_____

Progress chart   English and Verbal Reasoning 8–9 years

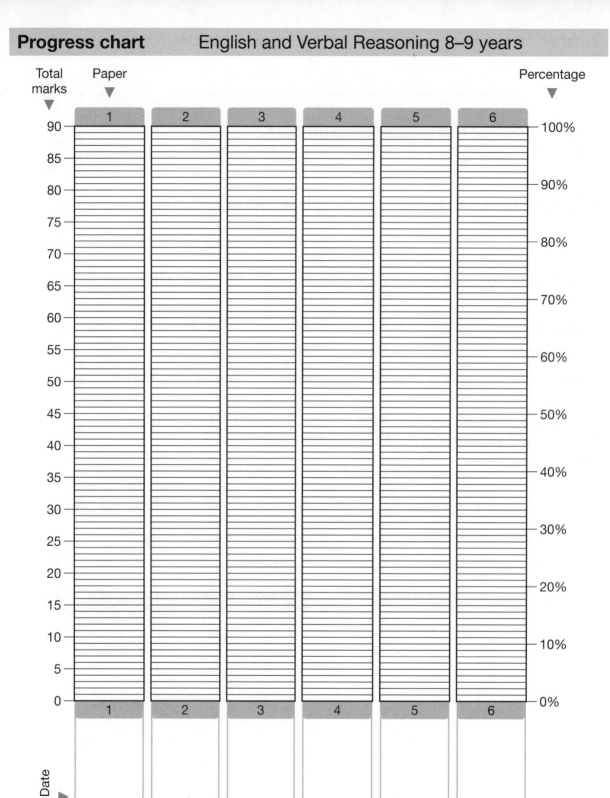

Total marks ▼

Paper ▼

Percentage ▼

When you've finished the book use the *Next Steps Planner*